The Novello Youth Choir

C000217346

Choral Anthology

For SATB Choir With Piano Accompaniment

Novello Publishing Limited
London / New York / Paris / Sydney / Copenhagen / Berlin / Madrid / Tokyo

Published by:
Novello Publishing Limited
8/9 Frith Street, London W I D 3JB, England.

Exclusive distributors:
Music Sales Limited
Distribution Centre, Newmarket Road, Bury St Edmunds, Suffolk IP33 3YB.

Music Sales Pty Limited
120 Rothschild Avenue, Rosebery, NSW 2018, Australia.

Order No. NOV078804
ISBN 1-84449-470-5
This collection © Copyright 2004 Novello & Company Limited.

Compiled by Nick Crispin.
Printed in the United Kingdom.

www.musicsales.com

Angels

Words & Music by Robbie Williams & Guy Chambers

when we're grey and old?_____   'Cos I have been__

Dmaj7   A/D   G   A

Ah_____ that sal-va - tion___ makes their wings__ un - fold.__

Ah_____ that sal-va - tion___ makes their wings__ un - fold.__

Ah_____ that sal-va - tion___ makes their wings__ un - fold.__

told   that sal-va - tion___ makes their wings__ un - fold.__

Em7   G   Bm7

and I feel that love is____ dead,____ I'm lov - ing an - gels in - stead.__

and I feel that love is____ dead,____ I'm lov - ing an - gels in - stead.__

feel that love is____ dead,____ I'm lov - ing an - gels in - stead.__

feel that love is____ dead,____ I'm lov - ing an - gels in - stead.__

D   C   G

f *sempre legato*

And through it   all_____ she of - fers me__ pro - tec -

f *sempre legato*

And through it   all_____ she of - fers me__ pro - tec -

f *sempre legato*

And through it   all_____ she of - fers me__ pro - tec -

f *sempre legato*

And through it   all_____ she of - fers me__ pro - tec -

D

f

7

When I'm feel-ing weak,___ and my pain___ walks down___ a c

___ way street,___ I look a-bove,___ and I kn

_ I'll al - ways be blessed___ with love.___

10

Ah

Ah

Ah

as the feel-ing grows,   she brings flesh to my bones,   and

C   G/B

I'm   lo-ving an-gels in - stead.____ And through it   all____

I'm   lo-ving an-gels in - stead.____ And through it   all____

I'm   lo-ving an-gels in - stead.____ And through it   all ___

when love is dead,   I'm lo-ving an-gels in - stead.____ And through it   all___

D   C   G   D   *D. % al Coda*

11

Blueberry Hill

Words & Music by Larry Stock, Al Lewis & Vincent Rose

17

19

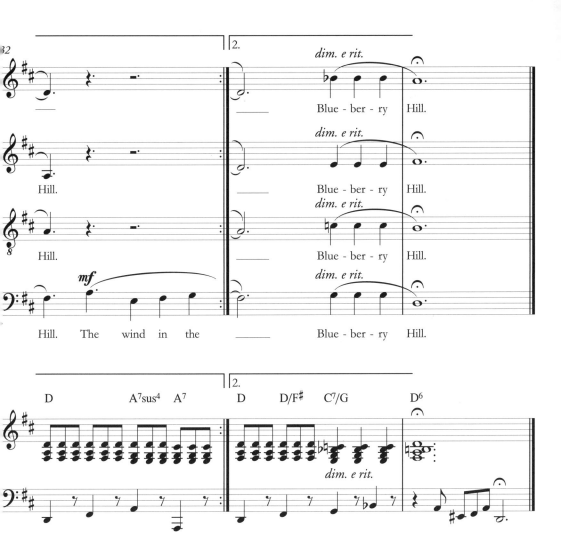

California Dreamin'

Words & Music by John Phillips & Michelle Phillips

(String Bass 8va as necessary)

25

1. I'd be safe and warm, _____   If I was in L. A
2. If I did-n't tell ___ her ___   I could leave__ to-day

1. I'd be safe and warm, _____   If I was in L. A
2. If I did-n't tell ___ her ___   I could leave__ to-day

warm, ___   If I was in L. A. ___
tell her _   I could leave__ to-day ___

warm, ___   If I was in L. A. ___
tell her _   I could leave__ to - day. ___

Dm   C   Bb   C   A7sus4

Cal - i - for - nia dream - in' on such a win-ter

Cal - i - for - nia dream - in' on such a win-ter

Cal-i-for-nia dream-in'_   on such a win-ter

Cal-i-for-nia dream-in'   on such a win-ter

A7   Dm   C   Bb   C

26

28

He knows I'm gon - na stay.____

He knows I'm gon - na stay.____

stay.

Cal - i - for - nia

He knows I'm gon - na stay.____

Cal - i - for - nia

A7(sus4)

A7

Cal - i - for - nia dream - in' on such a win-ter's day.____

Cal - i - for - nia dream - in' on such a win-ter's day.____

dream-in'__

on such a win-ter's day.____

dream-in'__

on such a win-ter's day.____

Dm   C   Bb   C   A7(sus4)

29

— Du du_____

— Du du_____

f

— Du du_____ All the leaves are

— Du du_____ All the leaves are

Dm   B♭   A7(Sus 4)

CODA

Cal-i-for-nia dream - in'   on such a win-ter's day, Cal-i-for - nia dream-

Cal-i-for - nia dream - in'   on such a win-ter's day, Cal-i-for - nia dream-

dream-in'_____   on such a win-ter's day, Cal-i-for - nia dream-

dream-in'_____   on such a win-ter's day, Cal-i-for - nia dream-

Dm   C   B♭   C   Dm   C

La Cucaracha

Traditional Mexican

17
tie - ne, por - qué le fal - ta di - ne - ro pa - ra ga
tie - ne, por - qué le fal - ta di - ne - ro pa - ra ga
tie - ne, por - qué le fal - ta di - ne - ro pa - ra ga
tie - ne, por - qué le fal - ta di - ne - ro pa - ra ga
D7
20
mf
simile
tar. Ta - da - da - da - da - da. Ta - da - da - da - da - da. Ta - da - da - da - da - da-
mf
simile
tar. Ta - da - da - da - da - da. Ta - da - da - da - da - da. Ta - da - da - da - da - da-
tar.
tar. Da, da.
G G/F Eb7
mp

39

42

43

Dream A Little Dream Of Me

Words by Gus Kahn
Music by Wilbur Schwandt & Fabian Andre

Ooh_____

Night bree - zes seem to whis - per,___ "I love you,"___

Ooh_____

Ooh_____

G/B   Bbdim7   E7/B   Ddim7

Ooh_____   Ooh_____

birds   sing - ing in the sy - ca - more___ tree,___

Ooh_____   Ooh_____

Ooh_____   Ooh_____

Am/C   Cm(#6)

47

48

just say - ing__ this:__

just__ say - ing__ this:__

just say - ing__ this:__

just say - ing__ this:__

Ooh__

Sweet dreams till sun - beams__ find__ you,__

Ooh__

Ooh__

51

God Bless The Child

Words & Music by Arthur Herzog Jr. & Billie Holiday

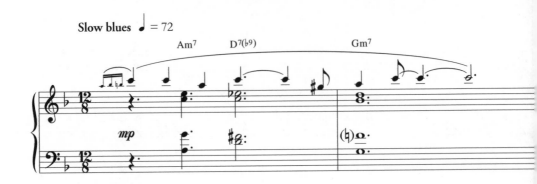

Mmm

Alto

Tenor

Bass

F⁷   B♭⁷   F⁷   B♭⁷

Them that's { got shall get,— them that's
{ strong gets more,— while the

Doo doo doo doo

Doo doo doo doo

Doo doo doo doo

F⁷   B♭⁷   F⁷   B♭⁷

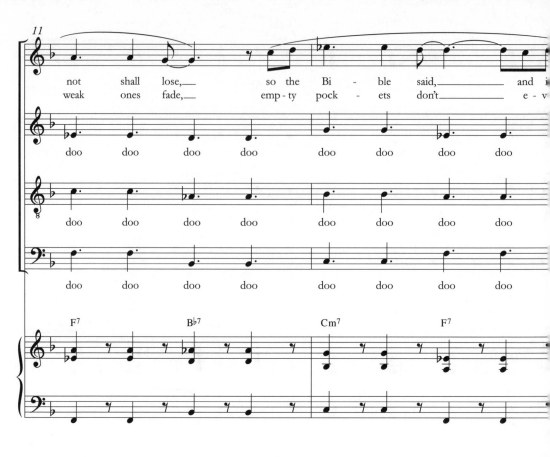

not shall lose,___ so the Bi - ble said,_____ and i
weak ones fade,___ emp - ty pock - ets don't_____ e - v

doo doo doo doo doo doo doo doo

doo doo doo doo doo doo doo doo

doo doo doo doo doo doo doo doo

F⁷ B♭⁷ Cm⁷ F⁷

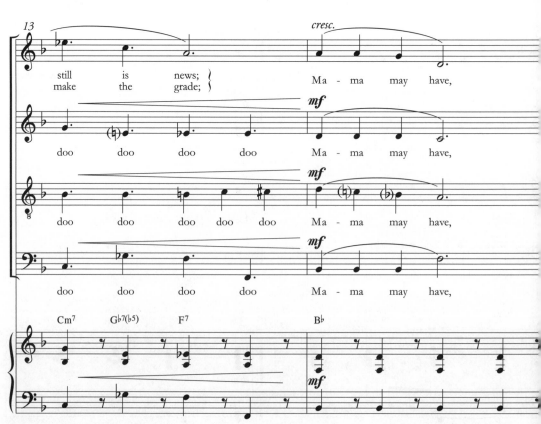

still is news; } Ma - ma may have,
make is the grade; }

cresc.

doo doo doo doo Ma - ma may have,
mf

doo doo doo doo doo Ma - ma may have,
mf

doo doo doo doo Ma - ma may have,
mf

Cm⁷ G♭⁷(♭5) F⁷ B♭

mf

58

Pa - pa may have, but God bless the child____ that's

Pa - pa may have, but God bless the child,

Pa - pa may have, but God bless the child,

Pa - pa may have, but God bless the child,

B♭m   Am⁷   D⁷⁽♭⁹⁾

got his own,____ that's got his own.____

God bless the child,   God bless the child,

God bless the child,   God bless the child,

God bless the child.

Gm⁷   C⁷⁽♭⁵⁾   F⁷   B♭⁷

crowd - in'___ round the door.___

Am   E aug   Am/C   C♯dim⁷

When you're___ gone and spend - in' ends,___

When you're___ gone and spend - in' ends,___

When you're___ gone and spend - in' ends,___

When you're___ gone and spend - in' ends,___

Dm   A aug   Dm⁷   Dm⁶

help your - self,_____ but don't take too much!

doo doo doo doo doo doo doo doo

doo doo doo doo doo doo doo doo doo

doo doo doo doo doo doo doo doo

Cm⁷   F⁷   Cm⁷   G♭⁷(♭5)   F⁷

cresc.

Ma - ma may have, pa - pa may have, but

Ma - ma may have, pa - pa may have, but

Ma - ma may have, pa - pa may have, but

M - ma may have, pa - pa may have, but

B♭   B♭m

God bless the child, God bless the child that's got his

God bless the child, God bless the child that's got his

God bless the child, God bless the child that's got his

God bless the child, God bless the child that's got his

own.

own. God bless the child.

own. God bless the child.

own. God bless the child.

(arpeggiate up and dow

Mamma Mia

Words & Music by Benny Andersson, Björn Ulvaeus & Stig Anderson

* May be shared by Basses 1 & 2 alternating every 2 bars
to help breathing during the constant quaver passages!

69

75

I Say A Little Prayer

Words by Hal David
Music by Burt Bacharach

O Happy Day

Traditional

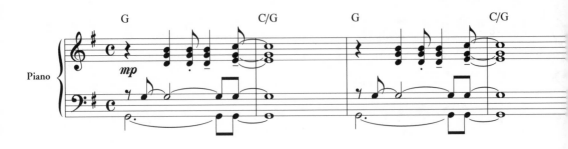

when__ Je - sus washed,_____

Ooh,__ when He washed,_____   He washed my sins__ a - way.__

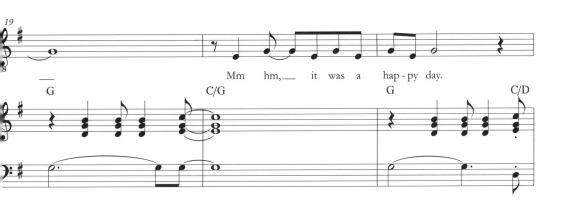

Mm hm,__ it was a   hap - py day.

93

Oh,— it was a hap-py day.

O hap-py day,— O hap-py day

O hap-py day,— O hap-py day

O hap-py day,— O hap-py day

O hap-py day,— O hap-py day

He taught me He— taught me how—

He taught me how— to

He taught me how— to

He taught me how— to

He taught me how— to

95

99

101

(Sittin' On) The Dock Of The Bay

Words & Music by Steve Cropper & Otis Redding

105

dim.
woh woh woh,
dim.
woh woh woh,
dim.
ten peo - ple tell me to do,
So I guess I'll re - main
dim.
woh woh woh,
3
3
E♭
C7
dim.
mp
Sit - tin' here rest - in' my bones,
And this
mp
Sit - tin' here rest - in' my bones,
And this
mp
the same.
Sit - tin' here rest - in' my bones,
And this
mp
Sit - tin' here rest - in' my bones,
And this
F6
A7
mp

lone - li - ness won't leave me a - lone.

lone - li - ness won't leave me a - lone.

lone - li - ness won't leave me a - lone.

lone - li - ness won't leave me a - lone.

B♭   G⁷

Two thou - sand miles I roam,_____ Just to

Two thou - sand miles I roam,_____ Just to

Two thou - sand miles I roam,_____ Just to

Two thou - sand miles I roam,_____ Just to

F⁶   A⁷

113

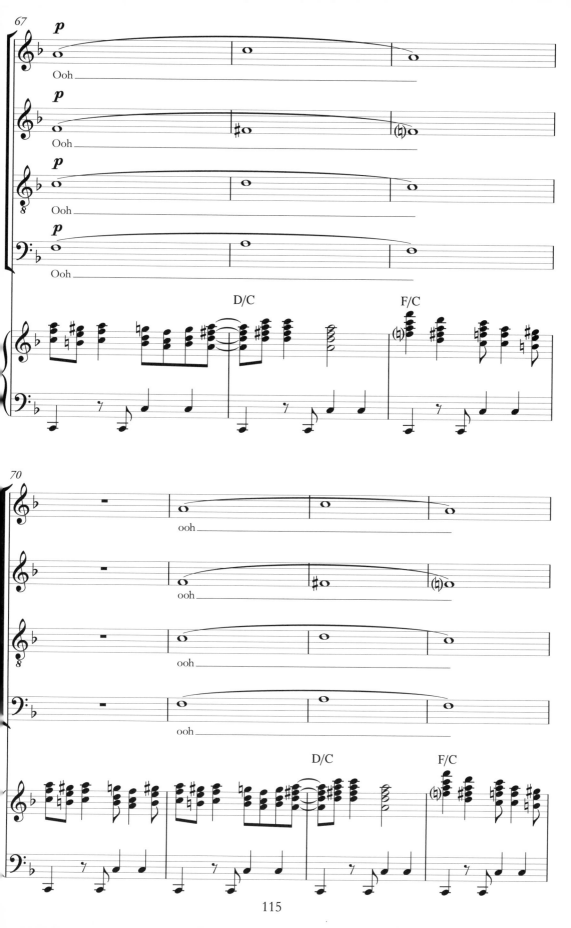

115

Swing Low, Sweet Chariot

Traditional

118

I saw a band of an-gels com-ing af-ter me.

home. Ooh.

home. Ooh.

home. Ooh.

home. Ooh.

Com-ing for to car-ry me home. Swing low, sweet

Com-ing for to car-ry me home. Swing low, sweet

Com-ing for to car-ry me home. Swing low, sweet

Com-ing for to car-ry me home. Swing low, sweet

124

Other titles available in the Novello Youth Chorals series for SATB